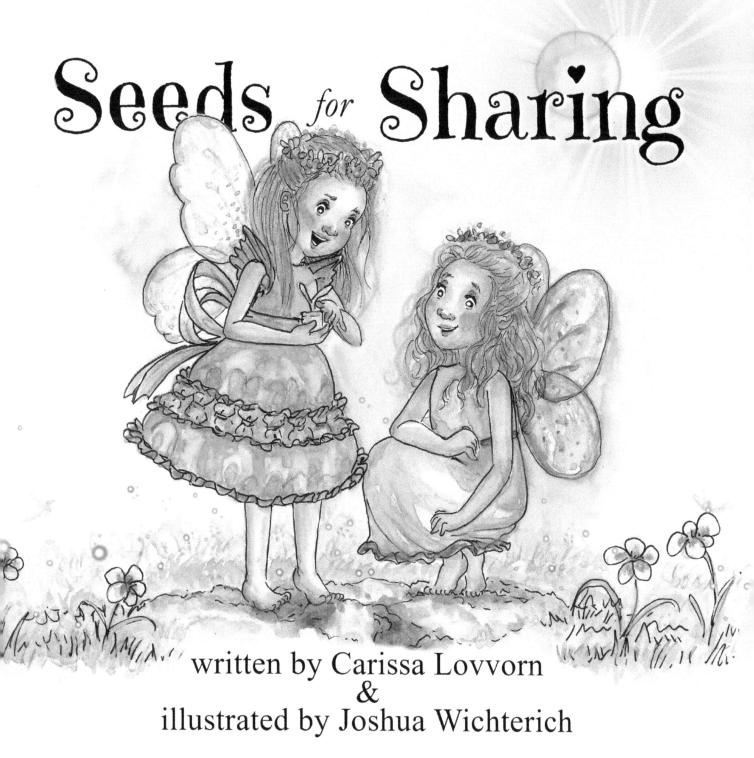

Seeds *for* Sharing

written by Carissa Lovvorn
&
illustrated by Joshua Wichterich

Printed in the United States of America
First Edition, First Printing, 2021

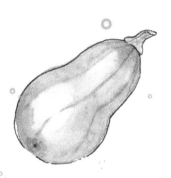

For my daughters, Isabelle and Ella

Thank you for allowing me to be a part of your magical world.

Always remember, when faced with life's trials

let your love, faith, and kindness shine through.

It was a dreary March day when the school was shut down.
The girls were sad without their friends around.

Their momma wiped big tears from their eyes and said,
"I know something that will pass the time."

Momma pulled out the potting soil, tray, and seeds and said,
"Let's get to work. Let's meet some needs."

The girls spent all day sowing seeds in the sun.
Who knew that gardening could be so much fun?

Each day the girls watered and sang to their plants,
until it was time to move them to the fence.

Up came the weeds and out came the hoe,
the girls were ready to see their plants grow.

They watched the blooms open and touched their bright flowers.
The girls prayed for sun and warm summer showers.

Then the day came when a small veggie emerged.
Such a blessing for them that their prayers had been heard!

The garden grew until it was ready to be picked,
most days they gathered much more than would fit!

Momma said, "Let's share. Let's spread some of our love!
And make sure we thank the Lord up above!"

With wings on their backs and masks on their faces,
they delivered their treasures to many special places.

The once sad little girls then became happy garden fairies,
while learning a lesson about God's love and sharing.

1 Timothy 6:18-19

18. Let them do good, that they be rich in good works, ready to give, willing to share, 19. storing up for themselves a good foundation for the time to come, that they may lay hold on eternal life.
(New King James Version)

CPSIA information can be obtained
at www.ICGtesting.com
Printed in the USA
BVHW060809150221
600140BV00007B/30

9 781736 382202